SEDUCTION

A Conceptual Model in the Drug Dependencies
and Other Contagious Ills

SEDUCTION

A Conceptual Model in the Drug Dependencies and Other Contagious Ills

By

PAUL H. BLACHLY, M.D.

Professor of Psychiatry
University of Oregon Medical School
Portland, Oregon

CHARLES C THOMAS • PUBLISHER
Springfield • Illinois • U.S.A.

Published and Distributed Throughout the World by
CHARLES C THOMAS • PUBLISHER
BANNERSTONE HOUSE
301-327 East Lawrence Avenue, Springfield, Illinois, U.S.A.
NATCHEZ PLANTATION HOUSE
735 North Atlantic Boulevard, Fort Lauderdale, Florida, U.S.A.

With THOMAS BOOKS *careful attention is given to all details of
manufacturing and design. It is the Publisher's desire to present books
that are satisfactory as to their physical qualities and artistic possibili-
ties and appropriate for their particular use.* THOMAS BOOKS *will
be true to those laws of quality that assure a good name and good will.*

Printed in the United States of America
Q-1

Acknowledgments

Permission to reproduce the cartoon "I Can Cure You," drawn by Abner Dean, was obtained through purchase from Julian Bach, Jr. Literary Agency; permission to reproduce the three drawings in Figure 5, "The Addiction Cycle," drawn by Jean Cocteau, was obtained through purchase from Howard Moorepark Literary Agent; permission to reproduce Table 1 was kindly granted by Dr. Miriam Siegler and the publisher, Marcell Dekkar, Inc. (Reference 17), and permission to reproduce Figure 16 and the substance of Chapter 12 was granted from *Hospital Medicine*, where it appeared in Vol. 5, No. 9, September, 1969.

Special thanks are due to Abraham Wikler, M.D., Professor, Department of Psychiatry, University of Kentucky Medical School, Louisville, Kentucky, for providing a concise formulation of the psychological conditioning factors in addiction, as well as for the model he has shown over the years of rigorous scientific investigation of phenomena of addiction.

To Miss Jane Marnchianes goes continuing gratitude for stenographic precision.

Contents

SEDUCTION

A Conceptual Model in the Drug Dependencies
and Other Contagious Ills

I

Introduction

THIS DISCUSSION arises from dissatisfaction with the practical value of existing psychiatric, sociological, and psychological conceptions for dealing with behaviors about which parents and society are most concerned, behavior which is exemplified by the following sentences:

He knows that it is wrong but does it anyway.
She agrees that it is dangerous but tries it anyway.
They recognize that it is destructive but persist in it anyway.
They acknowledge that it is harmful but indulge in it anyway.

These behaviors involve volitional, educational, and moral features, in contrast to that which has traditionally been considered mental illness.

The following behaviors are among those included:

Drug abuse	Suicide	Some marriages and divorces
Truancy	Gambling	Shoplifting
Robbery	Sexual deviation	Smoking
Promiscuity	Alcoholism	Overeating
Rioting	Speeding	

The term "seduction" will be used to describe these behaviors. Although the dictionary defines seduction as "to

3

lead astray," we will define seductive behavior here as behavior which has the following four characteristics:

1. Active participation by the victim in his own victimization.
2. Negativism (knowing the usual adverse consequences of one's actions, but doing it anyway).
3. Short-term gain.
4. Long-term punishment.

Seduction is different from persuasion. For our purposes, you seduce yourself and you persuade others. Behavior that does not meet all four of these criteria will not be called seduction.

Associated with seductions are the following observations:

1. Persons vulnerable to one seduction are likely to be vulnerable to others. Thus, we can speak of *high-risk and low-risk persons*.
2. Persons vulnerable to seductions at one time may be resistant at others. We can speak of *high-risk and low-risk periods*.
3. *Group pressures* and *social contagion* are usually a factor in seductions.
4. The behavior is learned; it requires energy and skills. As such, it is rarely a problem among the mentally retarded or seriously ill.
5. Prohibition is unpredictably successful in controlling these behaviors, since it frequently augments the very negativism that is fundamental to the problem.

When teachers or parents refer a child to me because he is smoking pot or using speed, it is rarely the pot or speed that most concerns them. They are really more concerned about the whole complex of the seductions, such things as diminished academic performance, promiscuity, undesirable associates, dishonesty, and poor communication, which they feel will lead to life-long inadequacy, embarrassment, and financial drain to them.

Persons who try to remedy these behaviors are often placed in the position shown by Figure 1. The fact that there is intent to help by "therapists" says nothing about results of such help, even if they can attract many customers.

Drug dependence will serve as the prototype of the seductions in this exposition. In the next chapter we shall review some historical observations.

FIGURE 1. I can cure You.

II

Historical Foundations

Twixt Adam bit the apple 'til Junior took a fix,* world history and literature have been supported by tales of seduction. Traditionally, children have been introduced to such concepts early in life through folk tales, bolstered as they grow up by traditional readings in organized religion. *The Odyssey,* Greek plays, *The Bible,* works of Shakespeare, *Pilgrims Progress, Peter Rabbit,* and *Hansel and Gretel* rely on the drama of seduction.

The Wizard of Oz[1] is a case in point. As Dorothy traveled the yellow brick road with her three companions they came to a poppy patch. Although she quickly fell asleep from the intoxicating fragrance, she was carried by Tin Woodsman and Strawman (Fig. 2) to the other side, where she awoke none the worse for her experience. In contrast, Lion, who was seeking courage, fought desperately against the fragrance. But the harder he fought the more ensnared he became, eventually succumbing to a point where his friends all but gave him up for lost (Fig. 3). Valiant Dorothy (an early social worker) would not give up Lion, and through

---

*shot of dope

FIGURE 2. Some get carried through the poppy patch.

mobilizing the entire resources of the Queen of the Mice,
was able to make a cart and pull him out of the poppy
patch where he recovered (Fig. 4).

Ponder these points to the story:

1. Everyone, like Dorothy, will one day experience the effects
   of hard narcotics. They are used routinely by surgeons in
   almost every operation. Even if you have had no opera-
   tions yet, your mother likely had her pains relieved by
   narcotics when you were born. You likely came into the
   world somewhat under the influence of narcotics! Yet,
   rarely do persons become addicted through physical illness.
   Probably fewer than 1 per cent of narcotic addicts were

FIGURE 3. Others get involved.

FIGURE 4. Rehabilitation is expensive and thankless.

started from medical sources. Persons rarely become medically addicted because they are carried through the ordeal passively by persons who are strong and not themselves affected.

2. Consider that those who abuse drugs frequently accuse those who do not, the squares, as being hardly human, without flesh and blood, like Strawman and Tin Woodsman.

3. The one who got trapped, Lion, was the one who got involved. Remember, he was seeking internal courage, despite outward appearances of confidence and strength.

4. Efforts to rehabilitate Lion required a vast expenditure of energy. It is impractical to devote sufficient amounts of society's resources to save every victim by currently available methods.

5. Lion was not grateful to those who saved him from the poppies. Those who venture to treat the seductees must not expect gratitude from the beneficiaries of their endeavors. This stems partly from their lack of recognition of the seriousness of their predicament and partly from their belief that they could have done it themselves if they had "really wanted to."

So everyone travels a yellow brick road encountering various kinds of poppy patches. How do we salvage trapped travelers, and prophylactically equip those who are just setting forth? The existing theories by which society has been attempting to deal with the problems include the following:

1. Drugs are people substitutes. (People are drug substitutes).

2. Drugs gratify unconscious needs and wishes.

3. Conditioning theories of Pavlov and Skinner.

4. Other models of addiction.

Developed to deal with problems of drug dependence, these theories may be applied in most cases to the behaviors listed on page 3, (interchanged for "drug.")

We shall review each theory briefly in separate chapters.

III

Drugs Are People Substitutes (DAPS)—Corollary: People Are Drug Substitutes (PADS)

WITHOUT explicitly saying so, most therapists intuitively act as though drugs are substitutes for unsatisfactory interpersonal relationships. They observe that in practice there is less need for tranquilizing drugs when interpersonal emotional support is firm and sustained. They also note that most persons who abuse drugs start such behavior at a time when other efforts to solve their human problems are not satisfying. So when, through accident or design, such persons find that a drug relieves their dys-ease, they are apt to repeat it. For those who have developed habits of interpersonal negotiation which are tedious and unrewarding, the highly predictable drug effects seem near miraculous. Once he finds that he likes drugs better than people, people are necessary only to the extent that they can be manipulated to satisfy his drug craving. Because drug pleasures are so much more predictable than people pleasures, in fact may be quantified by dose, in a free choice setting, the addict will choose drugs over psychotherapy. If "happiness

13

can be carried around in a vest pocket" as DeQuincey[2] said
160 years ago, only a masochist would choose therapy after
experiencing drugs. In short:

1. People get sick over people.
2. Drugs are people substitutes.
3. Drugs are more predictable than people.
4. People become needed only to supply drug craving.

In return, people resent the user much as the fabled ant
resented the grasshopper, even if they have not been per-
sonally robbed or conned.

Not only are drugs people substitutes, but early in the
game they are used as a topic of conversation no differently
than other people speak of golf, fishing, or bridge. Indeed,
addicts will distinguish between the user who uses drug
talk as a means of improving his people pleasures from the
"true hype" for whom people pleasurers are secondary. But
conversion from the former condition to the "true hype" is
all too common, as many a spouse of a junkie will attest.

The dys-ease may range from the malaise of the poverty
stricken adolescent turning to heroin, the depression of the
middle-aged professional turning to alcohol or sleeping
pills, to the unsatified drive for achievement by the graduate
student user of amphetamines. The drug used and the socio-
cultural background of the user may be extremely diverse.
The drug first used may not be satisfactory, and the person
may experiment with a variety of drugs until he either finds
one that meets his needs or gives up drug seeking as a way
of handling his dys-ease. But when his experience with the
drug and the people from whom he obtains drugs help him
to allay his discomfort, he is in a position where the probability of his repeating the use of drugs is high. Guilt for utiliz-

ing drugs for relief of dys-ease is in part allayed by the gradual development of a paranoid stance which makes him a martyr against those persons who feel that drug use is undesirable. The drugs will relieve his symptoms in a variety of ways, depending on their physiological effects. If he suffers from chronic depression and anticipatory anxiety, he may find that heroin relieves these and provides a feeling of simply not caring in the presence of others. Amphetamines, through relieving fatigue and perhaps occasionally actually improving performance, may provide the ambitious person with increased people satisfactions. Although such an improvement is short-lived and gradually leads to deterioration, the memory of what it has done, coupled with the fantasy of what it might do, becomes more important to the person than does the reality of his actual performance. What is most impressive to the drug user is that the drug effect, at least at first, is quite predictable; he can turn himself "on" or "off" at will. It becomes an habitual shortcut for the tedious negotiations necessary to obtain unpredictable people satisfactions. It should not be surprising that with such control over one's feelings a delusion of omnipotence should gradually appear, for if one can turn oneself on or off, one may in fantasy also turn others on and off. Sometimes this takes the form of apparent altruism in the user giving away drugs to nonusers, in effect controlling them. Coincident with the development of the delusion of omnipotence, there may occur, sometimes for the first time, the development of a conviction about the purpose of life. This new-found purpose in life is simply to obtain drugs and repeat and perpetuate the drug experience.

Prevention of drug abuse by the DAPS theory involves

provision of a developmental history sufficiently satisfying that drug use is superfluous, combined with prohibition to decrease the likelihood of accidental contact.

Treatment by the DAPS theory requires drug abstinence so that the necessity of developing sustained interpersonal relationships can not be chemically bypassed. Incarceration, by whatever name, is usually required to produce abstinence. Once abstinent, an attempt is made to provide satisfying people relationships with a therapist. In the better institutions this may be as much as one hour per week on a one-to-one basis. If group therapy is used, it is hoped that contact with seven other unhappy addicts in group discussions for three to five hours a week will have reconstructive effects. After the patient has become motivated for sustained improvement outside the institution, he is released, hoping that he will obtain employment and further treatment.

Although there is some merit in this approach for some drug users in special situations, the belief that it is useful in governmental institutions established for treatment of addiction has not been supported by data. What little evidence exists as to its value suggests that it is not only worthless but it is harmful,[3] for it fosters an uncritical belief by expensive therapists that they are doing something useful. To think that one one-hundred-and-sixty-eighth of a resentful person's time spent per week with a therapist paid by a third party can make a significant difference in attitudes or personality structure can only reflect a delusion of therapeutic omnipotence.

But PADS is effective for some users where the new relationship is sought voluntarily and is close, demanding, and sympathetic, as seen in Synanon and Alcoholics Anonymous. Occasionally, it may be effective in those institutions that admit an addict to a ward where the remainder of the patients are psychotic or geriatric, for they at least will not be undoing the work of the therapist.

IV

Drugs Satisfy Unconscious Needs and Wishes, or Pharmacothymia

RADO[4] believed that it is <u>not the drug</u> but the impulse to <u>use it</u> that makes an addict of an individual. The fact that at least early in the game addicts frequently exchange one drug for another made him feel that drug craving was one simple disease he called "pharmacothymia." Pharmacothymia exists because drugs can produce euphoria, can give pleasure, and allay pain. The pleasure effect depends in part on an active psychological preparedness with which the individual approaches the experience. Drug users are usually educated about what to expect before they first try a drug. The fact that the person must pay for his pleasure effect with suffering and self-injury, even to the point of self-destruction, seems to go against all rules of human behavior that a person will avoid pain, seek pleasure, and learn through experience. To understand why the drug user cannot stop doing as he does, Rado noticed a consistency in the addict's past history.

He found that prior to drug use addicted persons had been tense, frequently depressed, and intolerant to pain

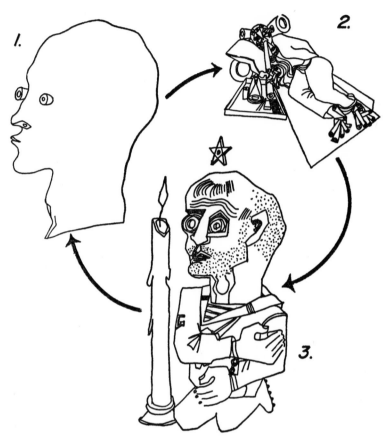

FIGURE 5. Addiction cycle. (Reproduced by permission through purchase from Cocteau, Jean, *Opium, The Diary of a Cure.*) New York, Grove Press, 1958.

(Fig. 5, Phase 1). This state made them receptive to any pleasure effect. If the dose of the chemical was appropriate, the resultant effects were highly impressive. Miraculously, the person was transformed from a tense, unhappy being to an euphroic, optimistic soul to whom all things were possible. But was the addict congenitally tense and depressed?

Presumably, as a baby he had experienced immeasurable self-esteem and feelings of omnipotence. The painful experiences of life shrank the infantile megalomania to a point of unpleasant self-devaluation. Yet, the memory of this delightful infantile narcissistic state lingered in the unconscious. Then, perhaps by accident, this miserable person learned that he could produce this infantile state at will by chemical or pill. It is as if the former stresses were a nightmare and he has proven his own ego omnipotent as he always knew it was. At the height of elation, respect and interest in reality disappear. All of the person's habits for dealing with reality painfully acquired during a lifetime are neglected. And all of the unsatisfied instincts may float to the surface either in fantasy or floundering activity (Fig. 5, Phase 2). But after the first few hours this effect wears off.

Reality becomes more painful than ever, compared with experience. In addition, there is a sense of guilt for having tasted the taboo fruit of infantile narcissism. As he feels progressively worse, the memory of the former grows more vivid. Only with the greatest effort of will can he renounce the idea of taking the drug just once more (Fig. 5, Phase 3). Although the first taste of the drug may have been accidental, it is the start of the second cycle that is the real onset of drug dependency.

But as time goes on the elation aspect of the drug use dies out and only depression recurs. A process of diminishing returns sets in: he cannot reproduce the effect with the same amount of drug, and drug intake must increase in order to compensate.

In the meantime, alterations in sexual life occur. Though

there may be a transient increase of potency, it soon wanes. The pharmacogenic pleasure dominates the sexual pleasure and there is a gradual return to an erotic or an infantile sexual model. Love objects are no longer needed, but do linger on in fantasy. In the periods between the peaks another anxiety develops, the fear of sexual impotence. Further, as the person gives up the demands of reality and sexuality by acceptance of the drug-induced passivity, he lays the foundation for an essentially homosexual style of life. (This feature may explain the very high ratio of homosexuals in the drug world.) This anxiety is simply added to other anxieties which make further drug use irresistible. As this cyclic course begins to deteriorate he feels confronted by two alternatives—a flight into involuntary abstinence or suicide.

In 1957, Rado[5] buttressed these ideas with the findings of Olds[6] that animals will prefer electrical stimulation of the pleasure centers in the brain to food, water, or sex. Thus, drug abuse results from a "superpleasure" analogous to such direct electrical stimulation of the pleasure centers. It is a malignant disorder because it corrupts normal hedonic self-regulation. Rado's prediction that biochemists could develop a drug which would "immunize the patient against the intoxicating pleasure-effect of narcotic drugs" has been fulfilled, at least in part, with drugs which block the pleasure effects of opiates such as cyclazocine, naloxone, and methadone.

Criticism of Rado's formulation stems from the fact that (a) his observations about the psychological makeup of narcotic addicts simply do not fit all addicts, particularly if one considers the nonwhite addict; (b) the value of reconstructive psychoanalytic therapy even for the psychoneurotic addict has yet to be demonstrated; (c) narcotic elation is not necessarily followed by sleep. Some addicts use narcotics to relieve pain and fatigue so as to function more effectively; (d) he fails to consider that a significant part of the guilt may result from the fact that the behavior is illegal: that it is a fugitive guilt rather than a guilt from tasting taboo narcissistic fruits, and (e) the psychoanalytic formulation is of no value in predicting the responses of animals to drugs, and therefore is not helpful in the evaluation of new drugs.

Prevention of drug abuse using this formulation seems to depend upon providing such a normal gratifying developmental history that drug effects are seen as undesirable or superfluous. The prevention of access to drugs thru prohibition must be relied upon for those who are vulnerable to drug effects.

V

Conditioning Theories

O F GREAT pragmatic value in the evaluation of new drugs in animals, and in suggesting new techniques of prophylaxis and treatment of human drug users, are the psychological-conditioning theories. There are two main types, Pavlovian and Skinnerian. In Pavlovian conditioning, the behavior emitted is conditioned by its antecedents; in Skinnerian conditioning, by its consequences. A couple of illustrations may suffice to make such abstract descriptions meaningful.

Pavlovian Conditioning[7]

If a dinner bell is rung regularly before each meal, a person may learn to have hunger sensations every time the bell is rung, even if later food appears irregularly. In this case the bell is the stimulus and it precedes the response of hunger. The physiological mechanism through which the perception of the bell is linked to the hunger behavior is the conditioning process.

Skinnerian Conditioning[8]

A person puts a dime in a candy machine, pushes a button and receives a candy bar, which increases the chance that he will use a candy machine again. In this case his behavior, putting in the dime and pushing the button, precedes getting the candy. Receipt of the candy may be considered the stimulus or reinforcement. Again, the conditioning is the physiological mechanism thru which the perception of the reward (candy) is linked to the memory of the antecedent behavior. The intensity, durability, and selectiveness of the conditioning process can be measured only indirectly through measuring manifest behavior.

Classical and Instrumental Conditioning
Theories of Wikler

Wikler[9,10] views drug dependency as an "instrumental" (or "operant") conditioning process, proceeding in successive phases, with changing "sources of reinforcement." In the earliest phase, when the future "addict" is experimenting with self-administration of single, isolated doses of various drugs, the sources of reinforcement are "endogenous," i.e. they lie in the patient's personality (anxiety, curiosity, boredom, anhedonia, anomie, hostility). Trying one drug after another, the future "addict" is likely to choose for regular (and perhaps exclusive) use, that particular drug which facilitates the mode of behavior he prefers to display in avoiding anxiety, et cetera. Thus, people whose preferred mode of behavior is aggressive but who experience anxiety when displaying aggression, are likely to choose alcohol or the short-acting barbiturates. These drugs, in doses customarily used, often "release" aggressiveness (not necessarily violent, but perhaps in the form of less-inhibited social interaction), and reduce anxiety, probably by the same mechanism. Other persons, preferring to avoid anxiety by preoccupation with their own fantasies, are likely to choose the so-called "psychedelic" drugs—marijuana, LSD, et cetera. Still others, preferring flight from anxiety in a state of reduced desire for anything, are likely to choose an opioid (e.g. morphine or heroin). DeQuincey,[2] Coleridge, and other mythologists to the contrary notwithstanding, opioids do not increase, they actually decrease fantasy in most people. In each of these instances and for the reasons mentioned, the particular drug of "choice" produces rewarding ("euphoric") effects for the chooser, thereby reinforcing further self-administration of that drug.

In the cases of certain drugs, i.e. those that do not produce "physical dependence," (marijuana, LSD, amphetamines, cocaine) the sources of reinforcement do not change except insofar as tolerance develops (except to cocaine) and toxic effects (e.g. psychoses) or disastrous social consequences make further use of these drugs less rewarding. However, in the cases of alcohol, barbiturates, and opioids, not only does the development of tolerance reduce the rewarding effects of these drugs, but they also engender the development of a new, "exogenous" source of reinforcement, namely, physical dependence (or "addiction"), characterizing the second phase of drug dependency. If, during this phase, the drug is withheld for any reason, distressing "abstinence phenomena" appear, which are promptly relieved by the drug in question, when it is obtained. Such dramatic suppression of abstinence distress is highly rewarding and hence reinforces further use of the drug powerfully. Furthermore, the "hustling" activity in which the addict engages to obtain the drug may add to the reinforcement of further drug use through the rewarding esteem in which "good hustlers" are held in "addict society."

In this phase, also, opportunities are often provided for another conditioning process that may be important in later "relapse after cure," namely, the "pleasurable" effects of these drugs could become conditioned to the physical and social environment in which the user habitually takes them before tolerance and physical dependence develop, the situation is quite different after tolerance and physical dependence are generated. In this phase, the addict is often acutely abstinent, and rather than the now greatly diminished "pleasurable" effects of the drug, it is the drug-specific abstinence phenomena that are likely to become conditioned to the physical and social environment. In keeping with this concept, Wikler[11] has shown that one easily measured sign of acute morphine-abstinence (increased frequency of "wet dog" shakes) can be conditioned to the external environment in the Pavlovian manner in the rat. Such a process could account for the statements occassionally made by opioid addicts that they experienced abstinence symptoms all over again, months after the opioid they had used had been withdrawn.

Sooner or later, the drug of addiction is withdrawn and now the individual passes into the third stage of drug dependence, "relapse after cure" (or "habituation").

> . . . relapse (or "habituation") can be viewed as a result of conditioning processes, operating in some different manners, depending on whether the reversion to drug use occurs "early" or "late" after withdrawal of the addicting agent. As long as some residue of "unconditioned" pharmacogenic dependence persists (possibly up to six months following withdrawal of morphine in man), relapse may be due simply to incomplete extinction of reinforced drug-seeking behaviour. Later, relapse may be initiated by recurrence of at least some fragments of the abstinence syndrome as a conditioned response, coupled with traces of previously reinforced drug-seeking behaviour

that remained as a result of non-extinction during previous episodes of addiction and "cure."

In relation to treatment, Wikler points out that mere withdrawal of the addicting drug does not result in extinction. What is needed to accomplish this is a program that will (a) allow the addict to "hustle" for drugs but prevent their having any "rewarding" or readdicting effects and (b) furnish competing, more socially acceptable rewards for purposeful activity. In relation to the first objective, the newly developed method of "cyclazocine blockade" (Martin *et al.*[12]) offers much promise.

It is only recently that the potential of Skinnerian conditioning procedures has been applied to evaluation of drugs of abuse in animals. In general, it appears that rats and monkeys will abuse the same drugs as humans, and indeed show much the same pattern of abuse. For example, just as in humans, in animals abuse of morphine tends to be continuous, but abuse of amphetamines and cocaine tends to be intermittent,[13] and as most any weekend "joy popper" will tell you—and in animals too—morphine can act as a reinforcer at doses that do not produce physical dependence.[14]

The major practical value of the conditioning theories may be to stimulate therapists who have been engaging in expensive, stereotyped, profitless therapy of addicts to try new approaches that can be worked out more quickly in animals. Some examples of this are as follows:

1. It has been shown that rats which are permitted to become readdicted in the same setting as their initial one become readdicted more rapidly than rats who are readdicted in a novel setting.[15] Clinically, abstinence makes the yen grow stronger, and in animals deprivation increases the strength of conditioned behavior. On these bases the hoary tradition of

incarcerating an addict for a few months and then returning him to the same environment might be viewed as a clear plot of the drug pushers to increase habit strength.

2. Habits that are developed where the frequency and intensity of the rewards are somewhat unpredictable are more difficult to eradicate than those where the rewards are highly predictable. Witness the power of the slot machine. The illicit drugs, being of variable quality, have this highly reinforcing "grab bag" quality.

3. The harder an animal has to work for his drug, the more ingrained becomes the habit.[16] The high price of heroin requires constant "hustling" to the point that an addict's entire waking activities may be spent in drug-seeking behavior in an addict culture.

4. Habits do not end abruptly. They extinguish slowly, often erratically.

If we wish to decrease habit strength and addict culture, it makes sense to provide addicts with drugs of constant purity at a fixed interval. The longer the duration of action of the drug, the less should be the habit strength. If the drug is cheap, the hustle will decrease, and along with it the addict culture.

Prevention by the conditioning theories would place little emphasis on developmental background at this time. Prohibition would be desirable. Efforts would be placed on relieving here and now factors that influence a person to judge drug effects as pleasant—boredom, anxiety, depression, hopelessness. (Animals to be conditioned to take drugs are first placed in a very boring isolated setting.) Problem-solving behaviors that would preclude drug-seeking would be encouraged, such as occupational advancement, romance, or political activism.

It remains to be investigated whether animals that are

raised under unusual circumstances, particularly where there is a dearth of succoring, will develop different strengths of drug dependence and different drug preferences from those of animals raised in normal surroundings.

VI

Other Models of Addiction

THESE three ways of looking at drug addiction—the psychoanalytic, the psychological conditioning, and the DAPS —have been discussed because they are most influential. But there are additional formulations, brought together most neatly in the form of Table I by Siegler and Osmond.[17]

TABLE I

	I. Medical	II. Socio-psychological	III. Moral Models				
			A. Retributive	B. Deterrent	C. Restitutive	D. Preventive	E. Restorative or Rehabilitative
1. Definition	Addiction is a chronic disease. The addict is a medical patient. Differential diagnosis is important but difficult.	Addict is a victim of social forces beyond his control. Addict is a person with deep-rooted personality problems.	Addict is a convicted criminal.	Addict is a bad example.	Addict is a debtor.	Addict is a failure in moral education.	Addict is a wrong-doer.
2. Etiology	1. Immediate cause: contact with addictive drug. 2. Pre-disposing factors: unknown 3. Chemistry: unknown	1. Presence of drugs and drug laws 2. Deteriorated urban slum neighborhoods 3. Disadvantaged families 4. Young people with severe personality disorders and sense of futility	Moral failure.	Lack of deterrence.	Not important.	Lack of moral instruction.	Moral failure because of the human condition.
3. Treatment	1. De-toxification 2. Maintenance dose or substitute drugs 3. Treatment of side effects 4. Restoration of general health 5. Rehabilitative measures	1. Social change 2. Psychotherapy	"Cold turkey" withdrawal. Punishment by imprisonment.	"Cold turkey" withdrawal. Severe, certain and public punishment.	Make restitution to victims and/or society. Example: work on public projects.	—	Confession, repentance, prayer, meditation, reality therapy, social rehabilitation.
4. Goal	Cure the disease, if possible, to restore patient to his previous state of health.	1. Change society so that conditions favoring addiction don't exist. 2. Bring addict to a state of health better than he had before.	Enforce the law.	Stamp out drug addiction by frightening people	Make sure that drug addiction does not cost society anything.	Prevent use of addictive drugs.	Abstinence from drugs, and re-involvement with society.
5. Prognosis	Addiction is a chronic disease. Prognosis if untreated: poor. Prognosis if treated with maintenance or substitute drugs: good.	Poor because: 1. Social change is hard to achieve 2. Psychotherapy is not successful with addicts.	When punished, the addict will know he has done wrong.	Addict and potential addicts will be deterred by fear of punishment.	Society will no longer be angry with the addict.	Incidence will go down.	Addict will become a new and better person, restored to society.

6. Function of hospital or jail.	1. Treat illness and side effects. 2. Educate patient about his illness. 3. Make plans with patient for continued treatment.	None: so-called hospitals are really jails.	To punish, so addict will know he has done wrong.	Punishment— show others what will happen.	None	—	No institutionalization needed. **Good atmosphere needed for rehabilitation.** A "retreat" or residential community.
7. Personnel	Physicians treat illness and supervise paramedical personnel.	*Not* law enforcement officers. Doctors, therapists, social workers, etc.	Law enforcement officers; they must be *fair*.	Law enforcement officers; they need not be *fair*.	Law enforcement officers; they must be *fair*.	Moral authorities; parents, clergy, youth leaders, teachers.	Clergy; therapists; the addicts themselves.
8. Rights and duties of addicts	R: To be treated like a patient with a chronic disease. D: To try to get well; to educate himself about his illness.	R: Humane treatment, social reform. D: None.	R: Fair treatment. D: Accept punishment, admit to wrongdoing.	R: None, not even fair treatment. D: None.	R: Fair treatment. D: Make restitution.	R: Moral instruction D: To learn	R: Not to be treated like criminal. D: Become a new and better person.
9. Rights and duties of addicts' families	R: To medical treatment for addicted family member. D: To bring patient to doctor, cooperate with doctor, educate themselves about the illness.	R: Humane treatment, social reform. D: None.	R: Fair treatment. D: Tell addict to accept his punishment.	None	R: Fair treatment addict to repay society.	R: A moral society. D: Teach the young.	R: Access to restorative facilities. D: Encourage addicts to rehabilitate themselves.
10. Rights and duties of society	R: To try to keep its members alive and in good health. D: To provide medical care for patients with this illness.	R: To be protected from crimes. D: Treat addicts humanely, to undertake social reform.	R: Retribution. D: Fair treatment for all addicts.	R: Drug-free society. D: Make an example of addicts.	R: Restitution from addicts. D: Set and enforce fair standards for restitution	R: Moral behavior from citizens. D: Teach the young.	R: See addict try to better himself. D: Not to treat addict like criminal.
11. History of model	1. Used in most Western countries, and in U.S. until 1914. 2. Recent attempts to revive it in U.S.	1. Used *before* Harrison Act. 2. Recent revival of interests by social scientists and psychotherapists.	In use since Harrison Act but never used fairly with *all* addicts.	In partial use since Harrison Act.	Never been tried.	In use since Harrison Act. Works with most people but not addicts.	Attempted sometimes. Recently: Synanon, Daytop, etc.

VII

The Integrative Value of the Seduction Model

Earlier we defined the seductive behaviors as having the following four general qualities:

1. Active participation by the victim in his own victimization.
2. Negativism (knowing the usual adverse consequences of one's actions, but doing it anyway).
3. Short-term gain.
4. Long-term punishment.

But these behaviors share a number of other more specific features. (Drug abuse is used as the model.)

1. *Drug abuse is a learned problem-solving behavior.* No person walks down the street, has a needle forced into his arm, and is thereafter an addict. All agree that drug users have known a good deal about drugs long before they began to use drugs themselves. Many are actively warned of the evils of drug using by other addicts. Through direct observations, and vicariously through mass media and books, they learn how to obtain, ingest, or shoot drugs. The victim actively or passively seeks the drug at a particular time for definable reasons.

2. *Drug abuse is contagious.* In most cases it is spread by a user providing access to a novice. The potential user is prepared for the overt drug use through advertising. Any advertising that generates much emotion regarding the behavior will tend to spread it, which may help to explain why scare techniques may increase the problem rather than decrease it.

Surveys of drug use in schools show that within the same city, some schools will have a significant problem and others minimal.[18,19]

For this reason the drug of choice moves in cycles and has fad characteristics. Drugs of choice at one time will be supplemented by others.

3. *Drug abuse requires certain mechanical and interpersonal skills.* It is not a problem for the mentally retarded or the psychotic. The intelligence of addicts is somewhat above average.

4. *Drug abuse requires energy.* It takes considerable effort to obtain the necessary money day after day to support a drug habit. It is for this reason that the seductive behaviors are most marked in late adolescence, and of little concern in the debilitated or aged.

5. *Education about the evils of drug dependency has not been a very effective deterrent to drug abuse.* It is true that many doctors have quit smoking because of the convincing data regarding its dangers, but it is equally true that a large number continue to smoke. Other forms of drug abuse are frequent among nurses, dentists, pharmacists, and doctors. To a definite but unknown extent such education with prophylactic intent produces a powerful effect—curiosity and desire for a direct drug experience.

6. *Failure of attempts at treatment and education have*

not stemmed from poor motivation on the part of therapists or educators. Curiously, often the harder such well-motivated people try, the worse the situation becomes.

7. *Enforced abstinence is of little value in itself.* Indeed, abstinence makes the yen grow stronger. Recidivism rates are so high that one wonders why we bother to lock people up at all.[20,21]

8. *Drug abusers are of widely differing personality types and originate from divergent cultures.* Or stating it differently, the personality types of addicts are as uniform as cigarette smokers.[22]

9. *The evils of drug dependence stem from two quite different sources*: (a) the effect of the drug on the chemical and behavioral makeup of the user; for example, death from an overdose, psychosis from amphetamines or LSD, lethargy from morphine and (b) the behavior of the user necessary to obtain his drug. In our culture this means burglary, prostitution, armed robbery, et cetera.

10. *A characteristic style of living and group of associates is usually implicit to drug dependency.* Every group that has a common interest develops habits in common that tend to protect and perpetuate the interest. Where the drive involved is as intense as drug dependence, and persecution is continual, the subculture will be proportionately strengthened, alienating further the addict from general society.

11. *Prohibition is usually invoked by society as a means of controlling the seductive behaviors.* Legal prohibition is a powerful weapon and, like most powerful weapons, is effective and useful under specifiable conditions. Under other conditions, it may aggravate the problem it attempts to alleviate. Prohibition is effective (a) when there is great public support for it, (b) when the proscribed behavior

represents a clear and present danger, (c) when that which
is prohibited is easily identifiable, (d) when the prohibited
substance required great technical skill and expense to produce, (e) when there is little profit in the substance or behavior, and (f) when there is no romance in the prohibited
substance or behavior. Prohibition is ineffective to the extent that these conditions are not met. Prohibition has been
tried and abandoned as effective control measures for such
behaviors as alcohol consumption, tobacco consumption, divorce, fornication, adultery, and gambling (in some states).

Support for the notion that drug dependency is a subclass
under the general category of seductive behaviors may be
gained by reflection that the following words may be sub-
stituted for "drug dependency" in the eleven characteristics
mentioned above with but minimal qualifications:

1. Smoking.
2. Suicidal behavior.
3. Delinquency, criminality.
4. Sex.
   a. Illegitimacy.
   b. Prostitution.
   c. Homosexuality.
5. Gambling.
6. Certain interpersonal alliances (marriage-divorce).
7. Risk-taking activities such as speeding, sky diving, some
   mountain-climbing.
8. Alcoholism (actually just one of the drug dependencies).
9. Rioting.

I am sure you can think of others.

Further, all of these classes of seduction have the inherent
characteristic of negativism. By this I mean that the victim
acknowledges the dangers of the behavior, at least for
others, but persists in the behavior regardless. *Any preventive education or treatment program that fails to take into*

account negativism as a major consideration will fail. It implies that educational information regarding the disturbing behavior per se, regardless of how fascinating, will not accomplish its intended aim and it may paradoxically produce vicarious gratification and practice of exactly that behavior which it hopes to discourage.

VIII

Graphic Portrayal of Seduction

To the aforementioned characteristics of seductions may be added their graphic description. They may be plotted by three overlapping curves as in Figure 6. The ordinate is the amount of behavior or activity that the seductee expresses or experiences. The abscissa is time.

The hump of the *Hustle* curve comes first. It is the investment with which one starts the cycle. Remember that the cycle was previously learned vicariously from colleagues, literature, or mass media. The hustle may be the nickle you put in the slot machine, the complex behavior involved in buying a pari-mutual ticket, or the money seeking and human interaction requisite to obtaining a drug. While to the eye of the spectator such behavior may be seen as punishment, to the participant it is filled with such anticipatory excitement as to gradually become rewarding in itself.

The reward may be as tangible as money, subjective as in relief of pain, depression, or sexual tension, or fantasied as in the accomplishment of a private intellectual agenda.

Similarly, the punishment will take as many forms as the combination of individual and seduction type can produce.

43

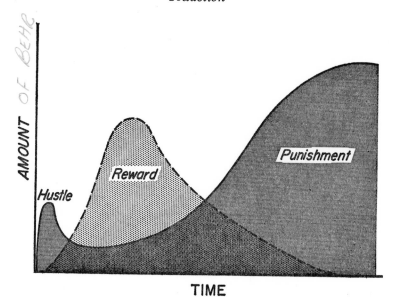

FIGURE 6. The Seduction schedule, prototype.

The ordinate and time scale depend on the seduction, the individual, and social context.

The effect of the seduction schedule on relatives and friends of the seductee may be plotted somewhat as in Figure 7. The hustle of the seductee usually provides some early reward to these associates, but is quickly replaced by increasing amounts of punishments. Line *A* indicates the course for a family member who can not separate from the seductee, whereas Line *B* might be the course of somebody like an employer. Line *B* diminishes slowly rather than abruptly, for the delayed consequences of the behavior of the seductee to the employer may persist through such intangible factors as loss of reputation and expensive delayed replacement of defective products.

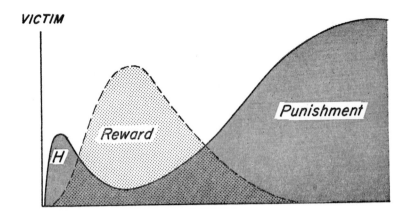

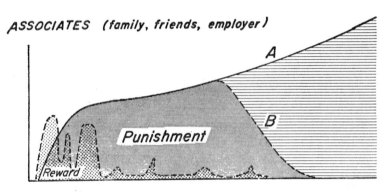

FIGURE 7. Seduction schedule, the victim versus his associates

Over the course of time the magnitude of the rewards and punishments changes as in Figure 8. Gradually one has to hustle more for less reward and insidiously increasing punishment. Such is the case for a heroin habit. But Aesop's fable "The Boy Who Called Wolf" is no different. Other seductive habits may spontaneously diminish over time,

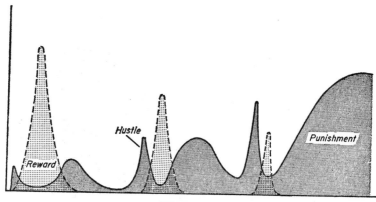

FIGURE 8. Change in size of hustle, reward, and punishment with time.

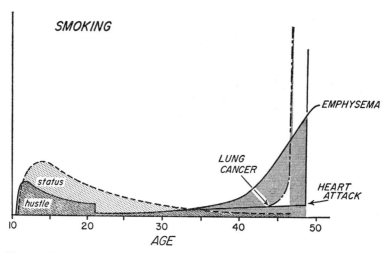

FIGURE 9. Example of low intensity hustle and reward—long-term extreme punishment.

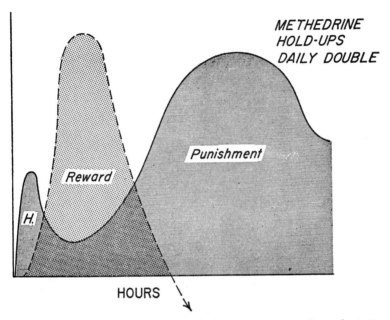

FIGURE 10. High intensity reward, less intense penalty—short irregular punishment.

such as glue sniffing and joy riding in stolen automobiles, as the fantasied reward is shrunk by reality.

An example is shown in Figure 9 of a seduction with a low-intensity hustle and reward, but a long-delayed but severe penalty—cigarette smoking. The hustle largely ends at age twenty-one, when smoking is entirely legal. The penalty may develop insidiously as with emphysema, more rapidly as with lung cancer, or precipitously as with a heart attack.

On the other hand, a high-intensity reward and less intense but prolonged penalty is diagrammed in Figure 10.

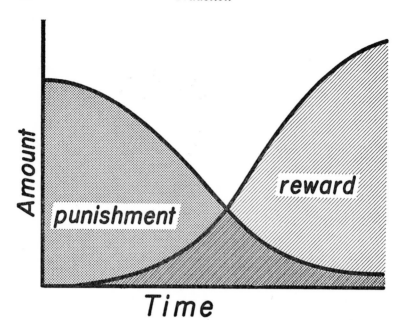

FIGURE 11. Schedule of construction.

The use of the drugs methedrine or cocaine, armed robbery, reckless gambling, and rape follow this pattern.

In the rehabilitation of drug users and other seductees, every effort is made to substitute a schedule of construction as in Figure 11 for their more customary seduction schedules. The construction schedule requires the deferral of gratification in the hope of delayed reward. It is, for example, the model we use in urging our children to complete their education. Undoubtedly, much of the difficulty in rehabilitating a seductee stems from the need to change from a fundamental seduction schedule of behavior to a construction schedule.

IX

The Seduction Threshold

How can we deal with the observation that we have all engaged in seductive behaviors, yet most adults engage in such activities rarely; a few seem unable to avoid them, getting in trouble repeatedly, seemingly unable to benefit from their experience? The implications of the fact that seductive behaviors are episodic like robbery rather than continuous like poverty have not been sufficiently appreciated. The significance of the episodic phenomenon lies in the fact that we can identify high-risk periods and high-risk people and take appropriate action.

Let us consider the concept of the *seduction threshold.* The seduction threshold is the likelihood at any specified time that a person will pursue seductive behaviors. Like a seawall, if the threshold is very high, only the spray from storm waves will get over, but if low, waves will be avoided only at low tide and fair weather. The common phrase "Every man has his price" refers to the universality of the seduction threshold, which implicitly recognizes that the "price" varies between people, and in the same person at different times. Figure 12 diagrams the seduction

49

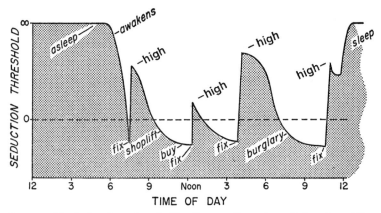

FIGURE 12. Seduction threshold of a well-motivated heroin addict.

threshold for a well-motivated heroin addict during a single day.

We see that while asleep the threshold is infinitely high, but that when the addict awakes suffering from drug abstinence it nosedives. He has to have a fix. But upon experiencing the drug-induced euphoria, he is safe—by which we mean that he will not immediately take another fix or engage in antisocial behavior. But this safety does not last, for the drug effect rapidly dissipates, and experience has taught him that he will need more drug. The probability that he will engage in antisocial behavior in order to get money to satisfy his drug hunger is directly inversely proportional to the seduction threshold, and soon becomes a certainty. Upon getting more drug he does not get a "high" but only feels "normal." He castigates himself for being dependent on drugs and wasting all of his money and resolves he will abstain. But time passes. As the drug effect wears off his seduction threshold lowers again to the critical

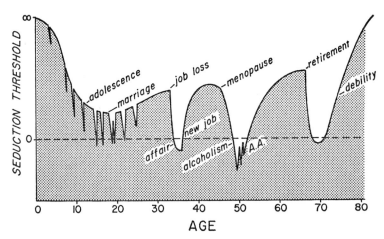

FIGURE 13. Normal fluctuations of seduction threshold.

point and he resolves that he will get enough drug so that he will not have to suffer so frequently. Therefore he engages in larger antisocial behavior, perhaps armed robbery or burglary, and with the increased money gets more drug, builds even greater drug dependency, et cetera.

We all know in a general way that there are times in the life of everyone when the seduction threshold is low, as shown in Figure 13. Such periods as adolescence, mating, job insecurity, menopause, and retirement are uniformly accepted as risky.

The seduction threshold of an adolescent boy confronted with divorce of his parents may be pictured in greater detail as in Figure 14.

Here we see that during confusion and depression associated with divorce when he is age twelve his seduction threshold falls. He has fantasies of hate, love, and grandiosity in attempts to compensate. In moving to a new neigh-

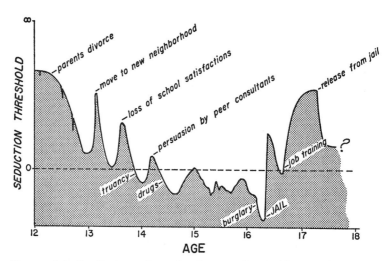

FIGURE 14. Predictive value of seduction threshold in a delinquent.

borhood he must give up old allegiances, but temporarily mobilizes his resources to assist the parent with whom he lives. But once over this short period, perhaps a week or two, the same discouragement recurs. Perhaps resumption of school provides structure and support, but without old friends and with continuation of daydreams, school performance fails, adding further loss. Truancy provides a seductive outlet and temporarily gives him increased attention, if only from truant officers. By this time he is associating only with peers in similar difficulty, and the advice he gets is thus the poorest rather than the best. At this time he is ripe for other quick solutions, and drugs provide a highly predictable though short-lived alternative. Magical qualities are easily ascribed to drugs, and it is easy then to turn the guilt around and say that it is society and the non-drug user who is at fault. One seduction leads to another, eventually he is caught for a major crime and is sent to prison. Momentarily he enjoys an enforced rise in his seduction threshold, but as he learns the ropes in prison, it again falls. Perhaps the structured environment with job training and predictable hours raises the threshold, but it will again fall upon release from jail.

The power of such representation stems from its ability to portray the probable consequences of the altered seduction threshold, and suggests preventive action. I submit that the parents, teacher, physician, minister, and police must do more than pick up the predictable casualities. They must take active steps to intervene at the points noted in the graph, steps which will insure that the seduction threshold rises.

X

On Generating Persons with Basically High and Low Seduction Thresholds

THE SAYING "A sucker is born every minute" refers to the observation that some persons get in trouble repeatedly, seemingly unable to profit from experience. Psychiatry has used terms such as "constitutional psychopathic inferior" and "antisocial personality" to label such individuals, conveying the notion of their resistance to change and suggesting a biological genesis.

Yet most studies suggest the seduction-prone individual is made not born. It appears that all of the findings of the Gluecks[23] with regard to the genesis of juvenile delinquency are pertinent to drug abusers and persons prone to other seductions. Using such factors as affection for child by parents, cohesiveness of the family, suitability of supervision, and consistency of discipline, they were able to arrive at a numerical value which would indicate the likelihood of delinquency by age sixteen. Impressive was the fact that their formula had predictive value before the child was six years old. *Perhaps the thread which runs through the Glueck factors is the extent to which a child can learn to predict the usual consequences of his actions.*

If through some malevolence we wished to grow a child with a low threshold of seduction, we would arrange it something like this:

1. Breed him to have a high energy level and predominantly mesomorphic body type, so that he will react outwardly to his environment.[24]

2. Have him taken care of by a variety of "mothers," aunts, grandmothers, baby-sitters, each of whom has a different style and expectations.

3. Discipline him erraticly and unpredictably. For the same behavior punish him one time and laugh the next. Children seem to be able to accommodate and discount consistently pathological supervision. Unpredictable "normality" is disconcerting.

4. As he grows older, every six months to two years, move frequently so that he will not be able to develop sustained allegiances. And if he makes wrong or right decisions, he will not benefit from their consequences, for he has moved.

5. Provide frequent family crises in which he is involved, but unable to influence the outcome. This will insure that he uses his mental faculties to adjust to the crisis, rather than building a solid intellectual foundation.

6. Have him associate with other seduction-prone individuals who will provide examples of short-term problem solving, without the guilt or satisfaction of those who live with their past.

7. During adolescence have him cared for by persons who will promise him the rewards of constructive behavior and the punishments of seductive beahvior, but who can predictably deliver neither reward nor punishment.

8. Given a child from a seduction-generating home, structure the school so that he can not form allegiances with adults upon whom he can model his behavior. This can be done by shifting him from one class to another every hour, transferring teachers from school to school, assigning a different counselor every term, et cetera. (We need give little effort to this now, for most schools already operate this way.)

Growing a person with a basically high seduction threshold is the reverse of the preceding. Essentially, it will optimize the child's ability to predict the consequences of his actions, and provide a digestable number of adults upon whom he can model his actions.

XI

On Distinguishing a Seduction Schedule from a Construction Schedule

"It is all very well for you to pontificate with the benefit of hindsight that one was on a seduction schedule. But how do you know, when you are actually involved, whether it is constructive or seductive? A construction schedule really differs from a seduction schedule only in that the punishment has not yet appeared. And everybody embarking on a seduction schedule claims that for him it is in fact a construction schedule."

These arguments must be carefully weighed. In some cases, as the drug dependencies and cigarette smoking, there is little problem of differentiation. But in such areas as business ventures and romance, the decision may be difficult. Here is where careful review of the four criteria of seduction are essential:

1. How emotionally involved is the person in the behavior? Remember that the victim actively participates in his victimization. The greater the emotional involvement, the more will he blind himself to counter arguments.

59

2. How does he use consultants? The second criterion, negativism, states that the person has prior knowledge of the
   usual dangers of his actions, but persists in the behavior
   anyway. Most seductees make little use of consultants, and
   choose poor ones, if at all.
3. What is the nature of the short-term gain? How much
   hustle does it cost? Odds-makers know that jackpots are
   rare and usually are an enticement to further hustle.
4. What is the nature of the penalty, especially to others?
   The seductee almost always is so egocentric that he fails to
   consider the consequences to others. This is particularly
   true of the alcoholic, the suicide, the divorcee, embezzler,
   and the person who permits blackmail.
5. Have his other behaviors followed a seduction schedule?
   Because a seduction schedule tends to be a life style, the
   record of previous performance suggests the future. In the
   stock market, "Those who buy high tend to sell low."

XII

Suicide as Seduction

SUICIDE angers doctors. For a person to take his own life when the doctor does everything to save it, is an insult, the action of an ingrate, and a polar rejection of the physician's philosophy. Therefore it may be easy for the doctor to try the civil liberties ploy, say that suicide is up to the individual, and wash his hands of the whole uncomfortable subject. Yet the facts are inescapable. Suicide causes more deaths than tuberculosis, syphilis, dysentery, scarlet fever, diphtheria, whooping cough, hepatitis, meningitis, appendicitis, congenital malformations, and asthma combined! Next to accidents it is the leading cause of death in college-aged individuals. And the wrong people commit suicide! The retarded, the incurably ill, the chronic psychotics, make up a surprisingly small proportion of suicides. Rather, it is the better students not the poor ones, the imaginative idealistic attorneys and doctors, the outstanding artists rather than dubs, who so frequently commit suicide.

Fortunately, though first angered by the suicidal patient, physicians now recognize that a person suicidal today may be most grateful the next day for being saved. The problem can be spelled out with some confidence in the sense of

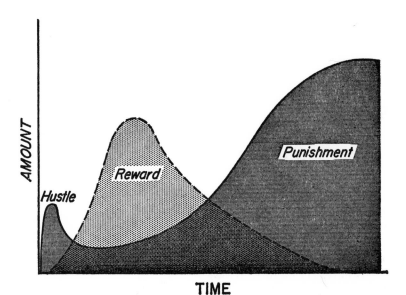

FIGURE 15. Schedule of seduction.

predicting high- and low-risk persons and periods. Let us look at two general principles.

PRINCIPLE 1. (Suicide is a special form of seduction.) Remember that seduction has these four characteristics:

1. Active participation by the victim in his own victimization.
2. Negativism (he knows it is wrong but does it anyway).
3. A short-term gain.
4. A long-term punishment.

Applying the seduction schedule to suicide, we see that the person who makes only suicide attempts or gestures follows the three-hump prototype of Figure 15.

His hustle includes collecting pills or a gun, threatening relatives or acquaintances, and other preparations. The re-

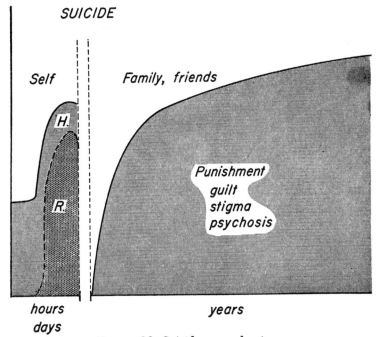

FIGURE 16. Suicide as seduction.

ward may consist of increased attention, successful manipulations of others, or revenge. Punishment may include bodily damage and gradual contempt or erosion of interest by the very persons he attempted to manipulate, much as in the fable of the boy who called wolf.

The actual suicide differs from the gesture in several important ways shown in Figure 16.

The reward is largely fantasied and is of short duration. The reward rarely exceeds the hustle. The punishment, insofar as we can be certain, occurs to relatives and friends, is permanent and stigmatizing.

That suicide conforms with the generalization that persons vulnerable to one seduction are vulnerable to others, seems confirmed by the high rate of suicide in alcoholics, drug abusers, and prisoners.

PRINCIPLE 2 (Suicide is a learned way of solving problems.)

Persons who have much experience with suicide and homicide seem to have increased risk. Suicide by a parent, spouse, or close friend is common in the history of persons who have committed suicide. The high rate of suicide by psychiatrists[25,26] probably reflects such increased experience, as does the suicide by the policeman with his service revolver. People use methods for suicide with which they are familiar. In one study 80 per cent of the doctors who committed suicide killed themselves with pills, while attorneys preferred guns or carbon monoxide.[27] Children, having little access to or experience with any of these, most commonly choose hanging.

Identifying the Potential Suicide

The person whose seduction threshold is low and who has learned that death solves problems is high risk for overt suicide, as well as for such suicidal brinkmanship as alcohol and drug intoxication or auto accidents.

We should watch out for individuals who are in turmoil, who are actively seeking to solve a problem rapidly, who have had experience with violence and death as a way of solving problems. I find that a question phrased, how did you learn of suicide as a way of solving problems? often evokes an interesting history and paves the way for exploring alternative solutions. Have they had relatives who committed suicide? Do they long to join a dead loved one?

Are they hurt and angry at someone upon whom they feel their own suicide could wreak permanent guilt?

We should be particularly wary of people who have a life pattern of doing what they say they will do. (Threats or allusions to suicide by a male over thirty-five are most serious.) Those who are compulsive and perfectionistic are especially dangerous, for although they may be depressed because of inability to attain self-imposed goals, yet they may plan and perform a perfect suicide at a moment when their seduction threshold momentarily nosedives.

The highly individualistic person estranged from friends or relatives is a high risk, particularly as he sees himself passing his prime. Should his inhibitions be dulled by drugs, alcohol, or postoperative brain syndrome, he may carry out a suicidal act impulsively, an act perhaps long nurtured in fantasy.

High-risk periods seem to occur from six weeks to six months after a major change in living pattern, such as divorce, death of a loved one, loss of job, change of home, or even major success. Susceptible persons should be "immunized" to such periods of lowered seduction threshold through frank discussion, education, and substitution of new satisfying thinking and interpersonal behavior. Turmoil and the need for quick, impulsive solutions may be produced by insomnia, chronic severe pain, disfigurement, financial insecurity, loss of ability to think clearly, depressed mood, and a host of other conditions.

Defining the Seduction Threshold

We must anticipate depression. If the doctor waits until the patient tells him he is depressed or suicidal, he will miss most opportunities to intervene. He must look at nonverbal behavior. Does the patient look blue, hopeless, confused, sad? Is his level of discomfort inappropriate to his physical pathology? Has he lost his job or family? Does he have no visitors? Is he drinking? Does the middle-aged patient who comes for a checkup seem unrelieved by the report that there is no pathology? We would ask, "At what level does his seduction threshold stand?"—while others have measured this in terms of lethality.[28]

Depression is inevitable when there is a loss of familiar patterns of thinking. The loss of goals, status, aspirations, faith, hope, or love may be more important than tangible losses of money or physical health. When illness dislodges familiar habits of thinking, the doctor should act on the assumption that depression *will* occur and should take preventive action.

When the physician is confident that hopelessness and suicidal ideation are just as predictable and susceptible to scientific investigation and treatment as heart failure or liver insufficiency, he will have removed the major barrier to aiding his patient's problem solving. When he utilizes whatever psychiatric technology is appropriate to that case, be it slower withdrawal of steroids, group psychotherapy, imipramine, convulsive therapy, or lithium, he will see improvement as dramatic as any that exists in conventional branches of medicine. And the lasting gratitude of patients for his assistance during this trying period of adjustment will have tempered the reflex anger evoked by the patient saying, "I don't need you; I want to die."

XIII

Group Seductions

THE HISTORY of civilization, if judged by its wars, is in large part a history of group seductive behavior. Military strategy is often successful to the degree that it can persuade the enemy to seduce itself. Although the principles and diagrams of group seductions are little different from those of the individual, they deserve a little elaboration thru examples:

1. The rise and fall of Nazi Germany.
2. The development of the F-111.
3. The Bay of Pigs Invasion and Vietnam.

Nazi Germany

The seduction threshold in post World War I Germany was low because of such factors as the following:

1. Economic anxiety, severe depression, inflation, and unemployment.
2. Failure of previous authority and father figures to be correct in their judgments. "The Kaiser lost the war."
3. An unstable previous history. Germany was welded together out of many subunits only late in the nineteenth century.

The reward fantasied was the removal of the anxiety, substitution of an infallible father, "Der Führer," and provision of a glorious and uninterrupted "Aryan" future.

The hustle consisted of national mobilization. Such purposeful behavior became a way of life in which the entire citizenry participated.

Rewards came promptly in terms of hope, relief of economic anxiety, and power over her neighbors, Czechoslovakia, Austria, Poland, France, and so forth. Such short-term rewards reinforce the arguments for the hustle behavior.

Subseductions easily gained ground within the larger fundamental seductions such as extermination of the mentally ill and the Jews, as well as the use of slavery.

Political organizations operating on a seduction schedule will attempt to get other political organizations to act similarly and often succeed, as Hitler did with Chamberlain at Munich.

The penalty of unconditional defeat and devastation affected not only Germany in which the seduction originated, but almost every other civilized country. Indeed, Britain at this point still seems to have suffered most from the war. Everyone loses with seductive behaviors.

The F-111

The saga of the development of the worthless plane, the F-111, at a cost of several billion dollars, provides a somewhat more complex and subtle example of national seduction.

The seduction threshold of the man responsible, the Secretary of Defense, was low for at least two reasons:

1. He prided himself on his managerial efficiency, eco-

nomy and general brilliance. If he could develop a plane which would be all things to all people, he would effect gross economies and prove his brilliance by showing up his advisors. Anxiety to the person in charge may stem from the impossible requirement to maintain an exalted position at all costs. The seduction threshold of a person coming into a new unfamiliar setting will be lowered by that alone. Adding to that the need to surpass persons already on their home territory provides elements likely to result in self-delusion.

2. Anxiety is often relieved by father figures. One way to make father happy, if he is a politician, is to make his constituents happy. And so the contract went to a Texas contractor over the objections of his advisors. Perhaps even *because of* the objections of his advisors, for negativism through enhancing the mirage of individual omnipotence is a part of every seduction.

The hustle in this case seemed to be the game of persuading others that the decision was correct.

The reward was entirely on the fantasy level to the man in charge.

The punishments accrued to the entire country in terms of such things as death of pilots of defective planes, loss of confidence by our allies in our technical ability, and obvious military weakness.

The Bay of Pigs Invasion and the Vietnam War

The invasion and the war had in common the fantasied reward of omnipotence so vital to a religious form of seduction. In both cases we would save the people (the minority) from themselves (the majority). The very intensity of the hustle (military preparations) contributed to the fan-

tasied reward. As with all seductions, persons were per-
suaded to support the war on the basis that it was the only
moral* course and that the long-term rewards far exceeded
the momentary gain. The tip-off that it was seductive behavior should have been that our usual consultants (allies,
United Nations) did not support us. We were supporting
ideological principles alien to our own (dictatorship and
state religion) and our centers of higher learning in general
opposed these actions.

Pre-Nazi Germany differed from the F-111, Bay of Pigs,
and Vietnam in that in Germany the seduction threshold
of the entire country was low, whereas in the latter examples the lowered seduction level seemed to occur in a
few men with great power.

A wonderful history of mass seductions is recorded in
*Extraordinary Popular Delusions and the Madness of
Crowds*,[29] written more than a century ago. Eric Hoffer has
dealt with this recently in *The True Believer*.[30] More re-
cent advertising techniques are reported in *The Hidden Persuaders*.[31] Mass financial seductions are periodically anal-
yzed in Barron's Magazine.

---

*Moral behavior refers to the acceptance of a short-term penalty for a
long-term reward, penalty and reward being determined by society's col-
lective experience.

XIV

Requirements for a System of Prophylaxis and Treatment of Seductive Behavior

LET us first outline some bare requirements of a system for prophylaxis and treatment of the seductions.

1. It should be applicable here and now regardless of developmental history of the individual.
2. It should be applicable to large numbers of persons by small numbers of "therapists."
3. Its efficacy must be testable through statistical techniques ✓ rather than individual testimony.
4. Its emphasis should be on prevention.
5. It must not rely on prohibition (not for idealistic reasons, but because of proven failure of most prohibition efforts).

For illustration let us take but two examples from the history of medicine. At the turn of the century, dysentery accounted for much death and illness of children in this country. Dysentery has been virtually eliminated not through the teaching of hygiene to school children, not through improved medical care of individual cases, nor even through development of antibiotics, but by invention and widespread use of refrigeration, coupled with sanitary engineering.

Infantile paralysis until a decade ago accounted for an appalling amount of disability and death among both children and adults. Efforts at quarantine and hygiene showed insignificant benefits. Much individual benefit and knowledge indeed accrued from heroic medical efforts directed at individual cases. Yet this scourge was eliminated, not through such massive noble efforts by armies of therapists, but by development of vaccines by relatively few people, which would immunize populations against this crippling illness, even when one is exposed to it. Can we immunize against seduction? Can we utilize principles developed here to modify seductive behaviors in people already involved?

XV

Immunization Against Seductive Behaviors

I<small>MMUNIZATION</small> relies upon the development of resistance
of the body to a small or mild infection produced under
controlled conditions to prevent serious illness from a severe
accidental infection. Immunization itself has small but definable hazards. For example, small pox vaccination carries
some risk, and rabies vaccination carries considerable risk.
Yet there is agreement that the risks of the immunization
program are so small in comparison to the unmodified illness as to warrant the procedures.

The concept of *high-risk periods* is important to immunization. We do not get immunized against tropical diseases
unless we plan a trip to the tropics. We usually get a
booster shot to prevent tetanus only after we get cut. Even
very healthy persons may succumb to an illness during *high-
risk periods*. But we can predict *high-risk periods* and take
defensive action.

High-risk *persons* are those who are likely to develop a
serious illness when others have only a mild case or none at
all. Asian flu vaccine may be recommended only for high-

risk persons such as those who are elderly or are already sick from other causes. Obviously a high-risk person in a high-risk period is doubly vulnerable. But we also know enough to define high-risk persons so as to take preventive action (Chapter 9).

Granting that we cannot protect people from themselves and from every eventuality, how can we immunize them against disastrous consequences of their behavior?

For example, how do we diminish the likelihood that our children will get into a car with a stranger who offers candy? Preferably, we start with a child with a high seduction threshold. Then we see to it that the physiological substrate of his seduction threshold is adequate, specifically, that he is not so hungry or candy deprived that candy will be an inducement, that he is not so cold and wet that a car will appear to offer protection, and that he is not so lonely that a stranger looks good. Secondly, we teach him of the possibility that somebody may try to persuade him to enter his car, and that there may be dire consequences therefrom. By teaching him that life has hazards, that he may be his own worst enemy, and that there are useful ways of dealing with such hazards, life is in fact made more enjoyable. The confidence that stems from knowing how to deal with predictable hazards vastly exceeds the benefits from unrealistic fantasies of ignorance. As with the fire drill, such learning occurs best with actual physical practice.

One can only speculate as to why concepts related to seduction receive little emphasis in contemporary elementary education, in view of the fact that they were so important in earlier years. Aesop's *Fables* largely depend on tales of seduction, for example, "The Fox, The Crow and the Cheese," and "The Boy Who Called Wolf." McGuffey's

Readers combined such teaching with basic reading skills. The concept of temptation is a theoretical cornerstone of religion, now little discussed. Thurber in his *Further Fables For Our Time*[32] gives seduction a modern humorous flavor, but students do not find him until college. The children's books with which I come in contact seem to ignore the real life observation that under certain conditions we may all be corruptible, that the bad guy often wins, and that the stupid suffer.

Adoption of the following educational activities within the home and school should diminish the chances of participation in seductive behaviors:

1. Initiate discussions as to why people hurt themselves and their friends and relatives. What are the circumstances that will make such behavior likely or unlikely?
   a. Have students think up and demonstrate examples of seductive behavior. Identify rewards, punishments, and time scales in the Seduction Schedules. How does the shape of the Seduction Schedule vary with different seductions?
   b. Have students distinguish constructive from seductive behavior; imagine how one may merge into the other.
2. Initiate discussion and research on what makes persons susceptible or resistant to seductions—identification of high-risk groups—such factors as the following:
   a. Geographic and social mobility, rootlessness, anomie.
   b. Multiple deprivations—family, social, financial, ego.
   c. Romance, fad, fashion, herd or group psychology.
   d. Depression, rebellion, negativism.
   e. Identification and imitation.
   f. People substitutes (drug effect more predictable and satisfying than interpersonal negotiations).
   g. Reinforcement schedules[8] (for advanced students).
   h. Philosophy, e.g. "Try anything once." "Those who

fail to learn from the experience of others are doomed to repeat it." "Eat, drug, and be merry." "If you haven't tried it, how can you condemn it?" (Homework on Greek "cynics" and "hedonists.")

3. Initiate classroom discussion and experimentation on how people change habitual forms of behavior.
   a. Incompatibility of two mutually exclusive behaviors. Substitution of nonseductive for seductive behavior, e.g. antabuse-taking and alcohol-drinking, cyclazozine-taking and heroin use.
   b. What is will power? Refer both to Skinnerian concepts[3] and to those of institutionalized religion.
   c. Experiments in changing habits, mannerisms, et cetera.
4. How does one distinguish use from abuse?
5. Student research projects on specific examples of seductions, changes of habit patterns, et cetera.
6. Use of role-playing, psychodrama, and antibrainwashing techniques.[33]

Conversely, we would *deemphasize* the following:

1. Education efforts at the high school and college level designed to give specific education and information about specific classes of seduction. This would include discontinuation of courses on smoking, drinking, sex education, drug abuse, et cetera. Such specific detailed information would be reserved for special student research projects, examples, and for advanced courses.
2. Movies, television shows, and articles that romanticize or excite interest in the specific seductions. Because of the imitative aspect of human nature, the fact that the "bad guy" or bad behavior loses may not compensate for the nonverbal message that one gains attention and sympathy through such behavior. To the contrary, one should create the image that involvement with the seductions is an incredible bore, the pursuit of the weak-minded and those easily "conned."

It is an assumption of some educators that information dispensed will be used by students to make rational decisions. The educator feels that he has done what is within his realm of responsibility if he has presented all of the information fairly. After that it is up to the individual to make a conscious choice. But, just as it is unwise to feed a person food he cannot digest, it is unwise to provide education that is not sustaining. Prohibitionists argue quite logically then that the ideal situation with regard to control of drug abuse is not present when the student can be offered a drug and refuse it but when the circumstances under which drugs are available never arise so that he need not spend his energies making a choice. But most communities inevitably thrust such a choice upon students and it is particularly in these communities where "immunization" regarding seductions is essential.

XVI

Treatment of Seductees

TREATMENT programs for those already drug dependent or involved in other seductions need considerable modification at least along the following lines:

1. Elimination of those well-intentioned and expensive activities not shown to have demonstrable value. This would include traditional across-the-board individual and group psychotherapy, vocational training and schooling. Such activities have unquestioned value in selected persons, but not for the seductive behaviors.

2. Active education of relatives, friends, employers to the fact that the seductee is able to continue his dependency in large part because of the mixed feelings of relatives, friends, and even employers who continue to bail him out of the inevitable sequelae of his seduction schedule. Such efforts at salvation in irregular amounts and at irregular times have all of the reinforcing properties of a game, and hence tend to perpetuate the seductee's style of life. Such ambivalently "helping" persons must accept the unpleasant reality that if they cannot help the seductee, at least they must not be an accessory to the addiction. As in the treatment of alcoholism, at this time science has no good alternative to total abstinence for many of the seductions. Until the seductee is willing to accept such total abstinence, activities of helpful persons contribute to the pathology.

3. Long-range research into factors that augment and reduce seductions. One example of an intriguing experimental program is the methadone maintenance treatment of heroin addicts.[34] Methadone is a long-acting synthetic narcotic which eliminates the "hunger" for heroin. By providing regular doses of methadone to such addicts it (a) eliminates all three humps on the seduction schedule, (b) eliminates the highly reinforcing natural variable-ratio—variable-interval schedule[8] of the addict life, (c) permits resumption of satisfactions derived from interpersonal activities, (d) diminishes the hostility to addicts stemming from the antisocial behavior requisite to supporting their habit.

Just as adoption of one seductive beahvior seems to lower the threshold for other seductions, the abandonment of one seduction schedule seems to facilitate abandonment of others. Thus, in the methadone program, we see that when persons give up some of their antisocial behaviors, they also give up others. From this point of view, you might be able to decrease shoplifting, for example, by getting the shoplifter to stop smoking cigarettes. Much more study needs to be done in this area to eliminate the fatalistic myth of the equivalence of psychic energy, such that if one does not rid himself of tension by one vice, it will express itself by another.

4. Development of effective alternatives to incarceration. If jail sentences effectively prevented further seductive behaviors, if penitentiaries produced penitent products, they might justify their extreme expense. Since such is not the case, we must become much more innovative in order to find treatment methods that really make a difference. Jail, fine, or probation do seem to be a terribly limited repertory of resources to deal with the incredible variety of people and behavior.

References

1. BAUM, L. F.: *The Wizard of Oz.* Grossett and Dunlap, New York, 1900.
2. DE QUINCEY, T.: *Confessions of An English Opium Eater.* London, Cresset Press, 1950.
3. BLACHLY, P., *et al.*: Group therapy and hospitalization of narcotic addicts. *Arch Gen Psychiat,* 5:393-396, 1961.
4. RADO, S.: The psychoanalysis of pharmacothymia (drug addiction). *Psychoan Quart,* 2:1-23, 1933.
5. RADO, S.: Narcotic bondage: a general theory of the dependence on narcotic drugs. *Amer J Psychiat,* 114:165-170, 1957.
6. OLDS, JAMES.: Hypothalamic substrates of reward. *Physiol Rev,* 42:555-604, 1962.
7. PAVLOV, I. P.: *Conditioned Reflexes: An Investigation of the Physiological Activity of the Cerebral Cortex.* London, Oxford Univ. Press, 1927.
8. SKINNER, B. F.: *Science and Human Behavior.* New York, Macmillan, 1953.
9. WIKLER, A.: Personal communication.
10. WIKLER, A.: On the nature of addiction and habituation. *Brit J Addict,* 57:73-79, 1961.
11. WIKLER, A., and PESCOR, F.: Classical conditioning of a morphine abstinence phenomenon, reinforcement of opioid-dringing behavior and "relapse" in morphine-addicted rats. *Psychopharmacol (Berlin),* 10:255-284, 1967.

12. MARTIN, W. R.: The basis and possible utility of the use of opioid antagonists in the ambulatory treatment of the addict. In *The Addictive States*, A. Wikler (Ed.), Assoc. Research Nervous and Mental Dis. Baltimore, Williams and Wilkins, 1968 pp. 367-371.

13. Pickens, R.: Self administration of stimulants by rats. *Int J Addic*, 3:215-221, 1968.

14. SCHUSTER, C. R., and WOODS, J. H.: The conditioned reinforcing effects of stimuli associated with morphine reinforcement. *Int J Addic*, 3:223-230, 1968.

15. WIKLER, A.: Conditioning factors in opiate addiction and relapse. In *Narcotics*, A. Wikler (Ed.). New York, McGraw-Hill, 1965.

16. WIKLER, A.: Interaction of physical dependence and classical and operant conditioning in the genesis of relapse. In *The Addictive States*, A. Wikler (Ed.), Assoc. Research Nervous and Mental Dis. Baltimore, Williams and Wilkins, 1968, pp. 280-287.

17. SIEGLER, M., and OSMOND, H.: Models of drug addiction. *Int J Addic*, 3:3-24, 1968.

18. JOHNSON, K. G., *et al.*: Adolescent Drug Abuse Survey. Section II. Sex, Grade, and Geographic Analysis.

19. SMART, R. G.: Drug use among high school students. In *Drug Abuse Now*, P. H. Blachly (Ed.). Springfield, C. C Thomas, 1970.

20. HUNT, G. H., and ODOROFF, M. E.: Follow-up study of narcotic drug addicts after hospitalization. *Pub Health Rpts*, 77:41-54, 1962.

21. VAILLANT, GEORGE E.: A twelve-year follow-up of New York narcotic addicts.
   I. The relation of treatment to outcome. *Amer J Psychiat*, 122:727-737, 1966.
   II. The natural history of a chronic disease. *New Eng J Med*, 275:1282-1288, 1966.

III. Some social and psychiatric charateristics. *Arch Gen Psychiat,* 15:599-609, 1966.

IV. Some characteristics and determinants of abstinence. *Amer J Psychiat,* 123:573-584, 1966.

22. HILL, HARRIS, *et al.*: Personality characteristics of narcotic addicts as indicated by the MMPI. *J Gen Psychol,* 62: 127-139, 1960.

23. GLUECK, S., and GLUECK, E.: *Ventures in Criminology.* Cambridge, Harvard Univ. Press, 1967.

24. SHELDON, W. H., *et al.*: *Varieties of Delinquent Youth.* New York, Harper and Bros., 1949.

25. BLACHLY, P. H., *et al.*: Suicide by physicians. *Bull Suicidology,* December 1968, pp. 1-18.

26. FREEMAN, W.: *The Psychiatrist: Personalities and Patterns.* New York, Grune and Stratton, 1968.

27. BLACHLY, P. H., *et al.*: Suicide in professional groups. *New Eng J Med,* 268:1278-1282, 1963.

28. FARBEROW, N. L., and SHNEIDMAN, E. S.: *The Cry for Help.* New York, McGraw-Hill, 1961.

29. MacKAY, CHARLES: *Extraordinary Popular Delusions and the Madness of Crowds.* Boston, L. C. Page and Co., 1932.

30. HOFFER, E.: *The True Believer.* New York, Harper and Row, 1951.

31. PACKARD, VANCE: *The Hidden Persuaders.* New York, Simon and Schuster, 1957.

32. THURBER, JAMES: *Further Fables for our Times.* New York, Simon and Schuster, 1956.

33. SARGENT, W.: *Battle for the Mind.* Garden City, New York, Doubleday, 1957.

34. DOLE, V., *et al.*: Successful treatment of 750 criminal addicts. *JAMA,* 206:2708-2711, 1968.